# GRADE E ... DE
# PIANO

GRADE **3**

## SELECTED BY
## IAIN FARRINGTON

VISTA
SCORE

BOOSEY & HAWKES

## Iain Farrington

Iain Farrington has an exceptionally busy and diverse career as a pianist, organist, composer and arranger. He studied at the Royal Academy of Music, London and at Cambridge University. He has made numerous recordings, and has broadcast on BBC Television, Classic FM and BBC Radio 3.

As a solo pianist, accompanist, chamber musician and organist, Iain has performed at all the major UK venues. Abroad he has given concerts in the USA, Japan, South Africa, Malaysia, China and all across Europe. He has worked with many of the country's leading musicians, including Bryn Terfel, Sir Paul McCartney and Lesley Garrett. Iain played the piano at the opening ceremony of the London 2012 Olympics with Rowan Atkinson, the London Symphony Orchestra and Sir Simon Rattle. He regularly performs with ensembles including the London Sinfonietta and the Britten Sinfonia, as well as all the major London orchestras.

As a composer, Iain has written orchestral, chamber, instrumental, vocal and choral works. He composed two orchestral works for the *Wallace and Gromit Prom* in 2012 including *Wing It*, a jazz guide to the orchestra. His organ suites *Fiesta* and *Animal Parade* have both been performed and recorded worldwide, and his choral work *The Burning Heavens* was nominated for a British Composer Award.

Iain is a prolific arranger in many styles, including traditional African songs, Berlin cabaret, folk, klezmer, jazz and pop. He is the Arranger in Residence for the Aurora Orchestra for whom he orchestrated all the songs in the *Horrible Histories Prom*. His organ arrangement of Elgar's *Pomp and Circumstance March No. 5* was performed at the Royal Wedding in 2011.

Published by Boosey & Hawkes Music Publishers Ltd
Aldwych House
71–91 Aldwych
London
WC2B 4HN

www.boosey.com

© Copyright 2015 by Boosey & Hawkes Music Publishers Ltd

ISMN 979-0-060-12767-0
ISBN 978-0-85162-938-4

First impression 2015

Printed by Halstan:
Halstan UK, 2-10 Plantation Road, Amersham, Bucks, HP6 6HJ. United Kingdom
Halstan DE, Weißliliengasse 4, 55116 Mainz. Germany

Music origination by Iain Farrington and Sarah Lofthouse
Piano performance by Iain Farrington
Aural Awareness recordings by Robin Bigwood
Cover design by RF Design (UK) Limited

# CONTENTS

**Note**: All fingering has been added by composers or arrangers or taken from first published editions. Fingering has not been added to pieces where such markings do not feature in the original source material.

 FULL PERFORMANCE & AURAL AWARENESS CD

The enclosed CD contains demonstration tracks for all pieces plus audio for Aural Awareness tests.
Track numbers are shown in grey circles.

# ROUND DANCE

## No 17 from 'For Children (volume 1)'

Composed in 1908–9, 'For Children' is a collection of pieces based on Hungarian and Slovakian folk tunes.
'Round Dance' has an expressive melody and the pedal is needed to link the left hand chords.

BÉLA BARTÓK
(1881–1945)

# AMERICA

## from 'West Side Story'

'West Side Story' – composed by Leonard Bernstein with lyrics by Stephen Sondheim – was premiered in 1957. In the musical, this number is sung by the Puerto Rican immigrants who discuss the virtues of America. The rhythms of Latin-inspired dance (especially the Huapango) are a defining feature of the song.

LEONARD BERNSTEIN
(1918–1990)
arr WILLIAM STICKLES

# O WALY WALY

The origins of this melody are uncertain, but it is well known as the musical setting for the folksong 'The Water is Wide', the lyrics of which date back in part to the 1600s. In the 20th century the tune became frequently used as a setting for the hymn 'When I Survey the Wondrous Cross', and Benjamin Britten wrote an arrangement of the melody in 1948. 'The Water is Wide' has been recorded by countless artists including Bob Dylan, Joan Baez and James Taylor.

Traditional English Melody
arr HYWEL DAVIES

# A LITTLE WALTZ FOR SONIČKA

Bohuslav Martinů was a Czech composer who wrote works in nearly every genre.  This piece is taken from his 'Children's Pieces' and is a charming waltz.  As the hands are so close together, clear articulation is needed for each note to sound.

BOHUSLAV MARTINŮ
(1890–1959)

# SCALE SPOT

**Gamelan Glimmer** (opposite) is written in the key of **A major**.
The A major scale contains three sharps – C♯, F♯ and G♯.

Practise playing the scale (below) – what fingering will you use to create a smooth and even sound?
Once you can play it *legato*, why not experiment using different phrasing and dynamics?

Here is an A major scale exercise.  Practise it hands separately and together.
When you're comfortable with the notes, try making the exercise your own by adding different dynamics and articulation.

The exercise below is based on a contrary motion scale.  The finger positions change at the same time in each hand.  Make sure you can play each hand smoothy on its own before you attempt the exercise with both hands together.

# GAMELAN GLIMMER

The gamelan is an ensemble of mostly percussion instruments from Java and Bali. It possesses a unique sound with tuning unlike that of Western music. Many composers have been influenced by these qualities, notably Debussy, Poulenc and Britten. This piece attempts to evoke the hypnotic sound of the gamelan: the pedal should be held throughout to blur the sound, the left hand should be played detached and with a bell-like 'ping'.

IAIN FARRINGTON
(b 1977)

# A SONG WITH A SAD ENDING

## from 'Fantasies for Piano'

Arthur Benjamin was an Australian musician who worked for much of his life in England as a composer and teacher. He wrote a considerable volume of instrumental and orchestral music as well as film scores, and found fame with such popular pieces as the 'Jamaican Rumba'. This work is taken from his 'Fantasies for Piano', published in 1933, and is in a flowing *siciliana* style. Good use of the pedal is required throughout.

ARTHUR BENJAMIN
(1893–1960)

# LAST TANGO IN POWYS

The tango is a Latin partner dance which originated in lower-class districts of Argentina and Uruguay (but not Wales!). It is marked by complex footwork, angular, passionate movement, and syncopated rhythms. Play this piece with attitude, making the syncopated *staccato* rhythms bold and spiky.

PAUL HUGHES
(b 1983)

# SCALE SPOT

Several pieces in this book (including the Shostakovich waltz, overleaf) are in the key of **C minor**.

There are various forms of the minor scale. The two most common are the **melodic minor scale** and the **harmonic minor scale**. The harmonic minor scale has the same notes going up the keyboard as going down, whereas the melodic minor scale changes depending on the direction of travel.

Here is **C melodic minor** scale:
(Note the A and B are naturalised on the way up, and flattened on the way down)

Here is **C harmonic minor** scale:

Practise the two exercises below with both hands together. Play them slowly at first.
Can you work out which version of the minor scale each is based on?

# SUITE FOR VARIETY ORCHESTRA – second waltz

As well as composing much symphonic concert music, Shostakovich was also prolific as a film and light-music composer. This waltz is taken from the 'Suite for Variety Orchestra' and was used in the 1955 film 'The First Echelon'.

DMITRI SHOSTAKOVICH
(1906–1975)
arr IAIN FARRINGTON

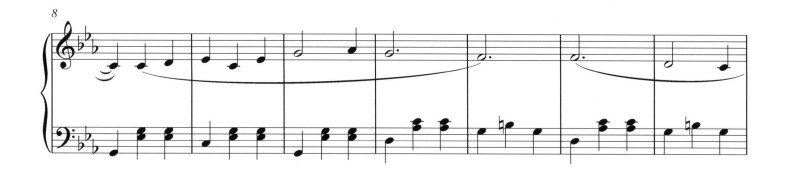

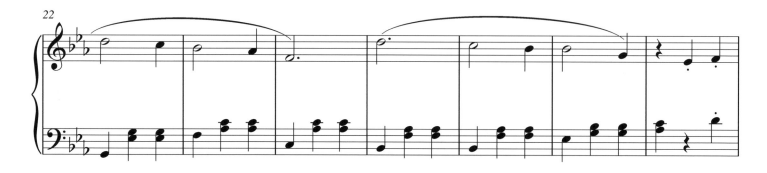

# SIGHT-READING 1

Look for the clues about how this piece will sound:

1. Take care to observe the accidentals. How many A♯s will you play in bar 7?
2. Is the key major or minor?
3. What does **Grazioso** mean?
4. Notice the time signature. Clap the rhythm of the music in the right hand at bar 2.
5. How should the last chord be played?
6. Note all the dynamic markings.

Set yourself a steady pulse and off you go!

PAUL HUGHES

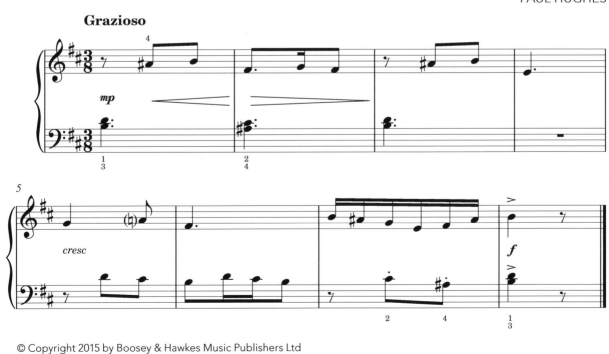

# PLAYING BALL

## from 'Thirty Pieces for Children'

Kabalevsky was an important figure in music education in 20th century Russia, and composed a large amount of children's music. This is from his 'Thirty Pieces for Children' from 1937–8. The hands should pass over each other, 'catching' the ball as it moves, with cleanly articulated repeated notes.

DMITRI KABALEVSKY
(1904–1987)

# WATKIN'S ALE

This piece is taken from the 'Fitzwilliam Virginal Book', a manuscript collection of nearly three hundred keyboard works by English composers that dates from around 1560–1610. 'Watkin's Ale' was a popular ballad from around 1590 with bawdy words. It should be played with energy and good articulation.

ANON

# AURAL AWARENESS 1

This activity will help you to better understand and enjoy the music that you hear and play. Like your fingers, your ears need a little practice, so try these activities with your teacher, listening to the CD, or to your teacher as they play the piano.

TASK A – MUSICAL FOUNDATIONS (18)

Listen to this short piece and see how many of the questions you can answer.
You will need to listen to it three or four times.

- Clap the pulse, emphasising the strong beats; is it in two, three or four time?
- Is the piece in a major or a minor key?
- Are the notes mostly *legato* or **staccato**?
- How loudly or quietly was the piece played? Was it the same all the way through?

TASK B – SPOT THE DIFFERENCE (19)

You will hear a key-chord and the tonic, followed by a short phrase from the same tune which will be played twice. There will be one change in the second playing.

- Is the change in the rhythm or the pitch?
- Describe the change, singing or clapping if it's helpful to do so.

TASK C – INTERVALS (20)

You will hear three pairs of notes from the melody – a low note first, then a higher note. Each pair will be played twice. Describe the interval formed by each pair.

There should be two parts to each answer:
1. the type of interval (major, minor or perfect)
2. the distance (2<sup>nd</sup>, 3<sup>rd</sup>, 4<sup>th</sup> or 5<sup>th</sup>)

(It might help to sing all the notes of the scale from the low note to the higher one that is played, counting on your fingers. The lowest note will be '1'.)

TASK D – CHORDS (21)

You will hear three different **triads** – each will be played twice. (A triad is a three-note chord – it's like an arpeggio but all the notes are played at the same time.)

After each triad, say whether the chord is major or minor.

TASK E – STYLE (22)

Listen to the piece you heard earlier one last time, and discuss anything else in the performance you noticed. Can you describe the musical style or mood, and tempo? What else do you observe about the dynamics and articulation within the music?

# A LITTLE SONG

## from 'Pictures of Childhood'

11

Aram Khachaturian was an Armenian composer who gained great success with his orchestral music and ballets, especially 'Gayaneh' and 'Spartacus'. This piece was composed in 1926 and is part of his 'Pictures of Childhood'. It has a very romantic feeling, and the sustain pedal should be used freely throughout.

ARAM KHACHATURIAN
(1903–1978)

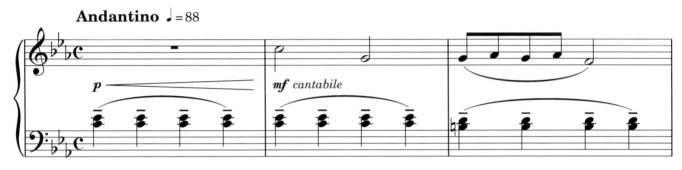

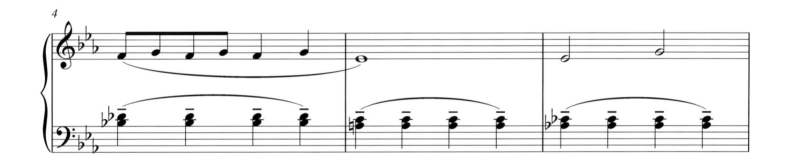

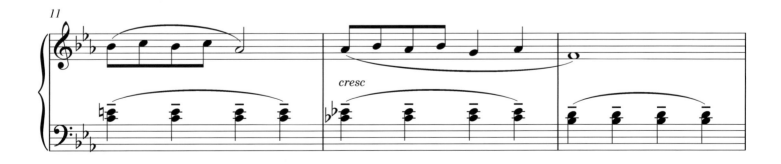

# CHILDREN'S DANCES – No 2

Zoltán Kodály was a Hungarian composer who was an important figure in music education as well as an active collector of folk songs. The 'Children's Dances' were published in 1947 and this one should be played on the black notes – imagine each note has a 'sharp' accidental before it.

ZOLTÁN KODÁLY
(1882–1967)

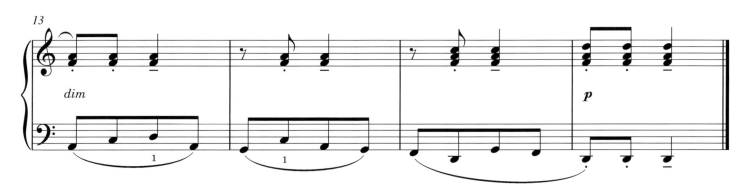

# IMPROVISE!

In this exercise we'll use some of the features of Kodály's **Children's Dance** (opposite) to create a pentatonic improvisation. (A pentatonic scale is constructed of five different notes. The black keys on the piano (C♯, D♯, F♯, G♯ and A♯) can be used to form a pentatonic scale.)

The left hand has a two-note ostinato pattern which should be played continuously throughout the piece. In your right hand, use any of the notes in the treble stave below (which are all black keys on the piano) to improvise a melody.

Improvising a melody in one hand whilst playing a repeating rhythmic part in the other can prove difficult at first, so don't be afraid to start simply. Begin by playing one semibreve note in the right hand every bar whilst maintaining the left hand ostinato. Once you're comfortable doing this, increase the frequency of right hand notes to a minim every two beats, and then a crotchet note on every beat.

When you're able to do this smoothly and without hesitation, you have all the tools you need to start shaping a melody:

–      Aim to use a variety of note lengths to give your melody a satisfying rhythm.
–      You could use all the right hand notes above, or just three or four. Remember that all melodies are constructed using a combination of stepwise movement and leaps.

Here are a few bars demonstrating how your improvisation might begin.
Notice the variety of rhythms used, and the contrast between stepwise movement and jumps:

# PICNIC PIECE

The composer writes: "A steady beat and *legato* lines in both the right and left hands will help create a relaxed mood. The **rit** at the end of the piece should sound inevitable; take your time and aim to reach gracefully a restful conclusion."

CHRISTOPHER NORTON
(b 1953)

23

# LONDONDERRY AIR

This traditional Irish tune was first published in 1855 after being collected by Jane Ross from the county of Derry. The lyrics of 'Danny Boy' by Frederick Weatherly were added to it in 1913. It is a passionate melody and this arrangement should be played with free expression and plenty of sustain pedal.

Traditional Irish melody
arr IAIN FARRINGTON

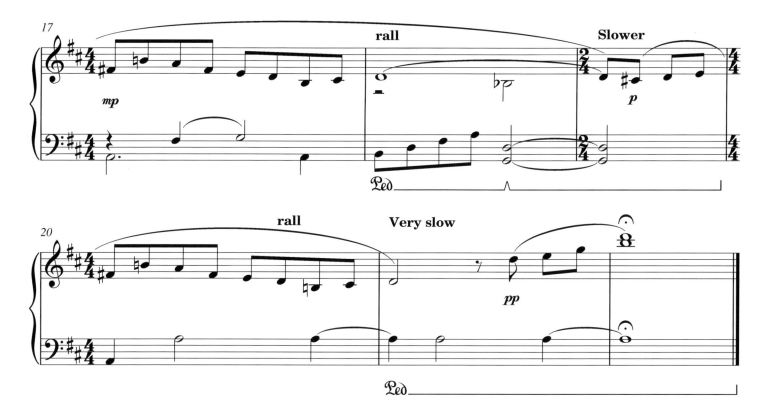

# SIGHT-READING 2

Look for the clues about how this piece will sound:

1. Is the key major or minor?  Name the key.
2. What do the following words mean: **Andante**, *leggiero*?
3. Clap the rhythm of the music of the left hand in bar 3, and the right hand in bars 3-4.
4. Note all the dynamic markings.  Which bar will be the loudest?
5. Describe the character of the piece.

Set yourself a steady pulse and off you go!

PAUL HUGHES

# SONATINA – first movement

Elgar composed his two-movement piano sonatina in 1889, and revised it in 1931. It was dedicated to his niece, May Grafton – eight years old at the time of composition. The piece has certain traits particular to Elgar, such as the flexibility in the tempo and yearning leaps in the melody.

EDWARD ELGAR
(1857–1934)

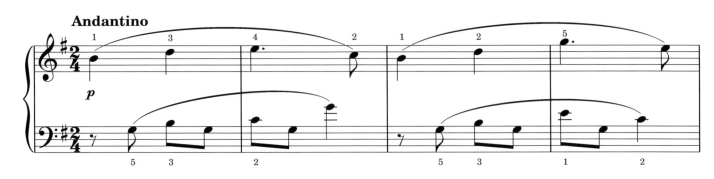

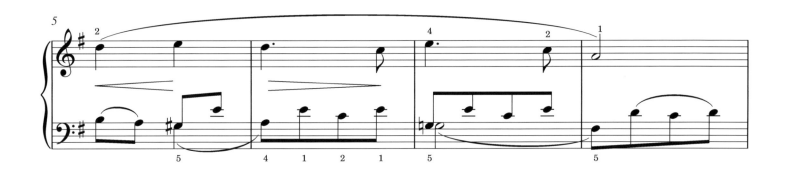

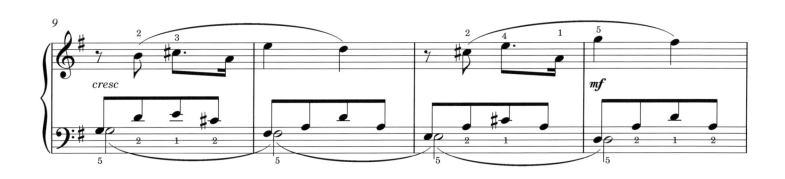

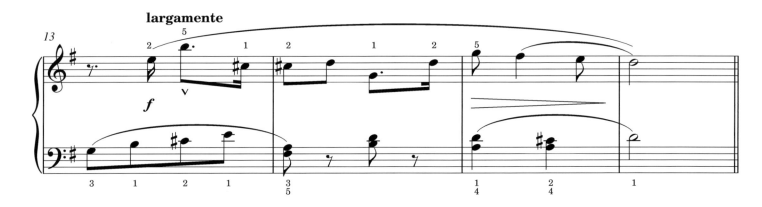

# BARWICK GREEN

## from 'My Native Heath'

**16**

Arthur Wood was an English composer and conductor from Yorkshire who composed much light music for orchestra. His suite 'My Native Heath' from 1924 includes the piece 'Barwick Green', which is a maypole dance. Its most famous use is as the theme tune to the long-running BBC Radio drama 'The Archers', first broadcast in 1951.

ARTHUR WOOD
(1875–1953)
arr IAIN FARRINGTON

**Allegro giocoso (ma non troppo)**

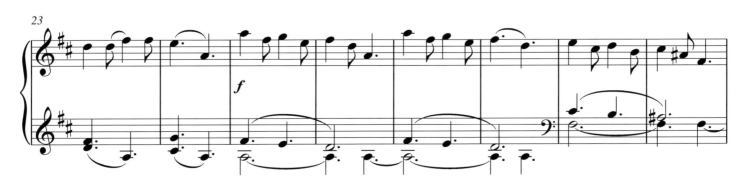

# AURAL AWARENESS 2

This activity will help you to better understand and enjoy the music that you hear and play.
Like your fingers, your ears need a little practice, so try these activities with your teacher,
listening to the CD, or to your teacher as they play the piano.

### TASK A – MUSICAL FOUNDATIONS

Listen to this short piece and see how many of the questions you can answer.
You will need to listen to it three or four times.

- Clap the pulse, emphasising the strong beats; is it in two, three or four time?
- Is the piece in a major or a minor key?
- Are the notes mostly *legato* or *staccato*?
- How loudly or quietly was the piece played?  Was it the same all the way through?

### TASK B – SPOT THE DIFFERENCE

You will hear a key-chord and the tonic, followed by a short phrase from the same tune which
will be played twice.  There will be one change in the second playing.

- Is the change in the rhythm or the pitch?
- Describe the change, singing or clapping if it's helpful to do so.

### TASK C – INTERVALS

You will hear three pairs of notes from the melody – a low note first, then a higher note.  Each pair will
be played twice.  Describe the interval formed by each pair.

There should be two parts to your answer:
1. the type of interval (major, minor or perfect)
2. the distance (2$^{nd}$, 3$^{rd}$, 4$^{th}$ or 5$^{th}$)

(It might help to sing all the notes of the scale from the low note to the higher one
that is played, counting on your fingers. The lowest note will be '1'.)

### TASK D – CHORDS

You will hear three different **triads** – each will be played twice.  (A triad is a three-note chord
– it's like an arpeggio but all the notes are played at the same time.)

After each triad, say whether the chord is major or minor.

### TASK E – STYLE

Listen to the piece you heard earlier one last time, and discuss anything else in the performance
you noticed.  Can you describe the musical style or mood, and tempo?  What else do you observe
about the dynamics and articulation within the music?

# PETER'S THEME

## from 'Peter and the Wolf'

Prokofieff composed 'Peter and the Wolf' in 1936 for the Central Children's Theatre in Moscow, and it has since become a hugely popular work for narrator and orchestra. Each character is represented by a different instrument, and Peter is depicted by the orchestra's string section. The tune is lively with plenty of attack.

SERGE PROKOFIEFF
(1891–1953)
arr CAROL BARRATT

# AURAL AWARENESS 1 (page 17)

---

## TASK A – MUSICAL FOUNDATIONS

Play the piece once and ask your student to join in with your piano playing by clapping in time as soon as they are able, placing an emphasis by way of a louder clap on the strong beats. Ask your student to identify whether the piece is in two, three or four time. Answer: This piece is in two time.

Now play the piece again, repeating as necessary, and ask your student whether the piece is in a major or minor key (major), whether the notes are mostly *legato* or *staccato* (*legato*), how loudly or quietly the piece was played, and whether the dynamics were the same all the way through. (The piece started moderately quietly (*mezzo piano*); it got a little louder (*mezzo forte*) towards the middle before getting gradually louder still (*crescendo* to *forte*). The dynamics decreased (*diminuendo*) at the end.)

ANON

## TASK B – SPOT THE DIFFERENCE

Count in and play both of the two-bar phrases below. Ask your student whether there is an alteration in the pitch or the rhythm of the second phrase and to describe the change using singing/clapping as necessary. Answer: There was a pitch alteration towards the middle of the extract; the fifth note was higher.

## TASK C – INTERVALS

Play each of the three pairs of notes below twice. Ask your student to describe each interval.
Answers: 1. perfect 4th, 2. perfect 5th, 3. minor 3rd.

## TASK D – CHORDS

Play each of the three triads below twice. Ask your student to describe each chord as major or minor.
Answers: 1. major, 2. major, 3. minor.

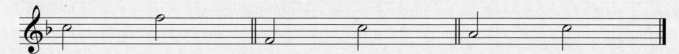

## TASK E – STYLE

Ask your student to listen to the piece played earlier one last time, and discuss anything else in the performance they noticed. Encourage comments on musical style or mood, and tempo, plus any additional observations about dynamics and articulation.

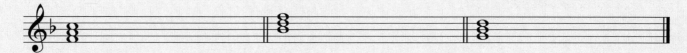

# AURAL AWARENESS 2 (page 30)

## TASK A – MUSICAL FOUNDATIONS

Play the piece once and ask your student to join in with your piano playing by clapping in time as soon as they are able, placing an emphasis by way of a louder clap on the strong beats. Ask your student to identify whether the piece is in two, three or four time. Answer: This piece is in four time.

Now play the piece again, repeating as necessary, and ask your student whether the piece is in a major or minor key (minor), whether the notes are mostly *legato* or *staccato* (*legato*), how loudly or quietly the piece was played, and whether the dynamics were the same all the way through. (The music is played *piano* initially, followed by a *crescendo*. Later in the excerpt there is a *diminuendo* back to *piano*.)

BÉLA BARTÓK

extract from 'Bartók for Children (volume 1)', no 34

## TASK B – SPOT THE DIFFERENCE

Count in and play both of the two-bar phrases below. Ask your student whether there is an alteration in the pitch or the rhythm of the second phrase and to describe the change using singing/clapping as necessary. Answer: There was a rhythmic change near the beginning; the seventh note was made longer.

## TASK C – INTERVALS

Play each of the three pairs of notes below twice. Ask your student to describe each interval.
Answers: 1. major 2nd, 2. perfect 4th, 3. perfect 5th.

## TASK D – CHORDS

Play each of the three triads below twice. Ask your student to describe each chord as major or minor.
Answers: 1. minor, 2. major, 3. minor.

## TASK E – STYLE

Ask your student to listen to the piece played earlier one last time, and discuss anything else in the performance they noticed. Encourage comments on musical style or mood, and tempo, plus any additional observations about dynamics and articulation.

# ALSO AVAILABLE FROM BOOSEY & HAWKES

*Round Dance (page 2) is taken from:*

**FOR CHILDREN** (Definitive Edition) – volume 1
Béla Bartók

ISMN 979-0-060-11230-0

40 Hungarian tunes for beginner pianists in a revised and re-engraved edition.
Includes an introductory note by the composer's son, Peter Bartók.

Volume 2 also available (ISMN 979-0-060-11231-7)

*Béla Bartók (1881–1945) was a Hungarian composer and pianist, recognised as being one of the most important composers of the 20th century.*

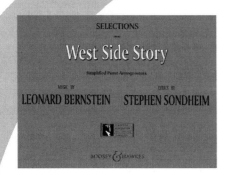

*America (page 3) is taken from:*

**SELECTIONS FROM WEST SIDE STORY**
Leonard Bernstein & Stephen Sondheim

ISMN 979-0-051-24613-7

A selection of five easy songs from the 1957 hit Broadway musical arranged by William Stickles for beginner piano.

*Leonard Bernstein (1918–1990) was an American composer, conductor, author, music lecturer, and pianist whose writing bridged the divide between classical and popular idioms. Stephen Sondheim (born 1930) is an American composer and lyricist known for his immense contribution to musical theatre for more than 50 years.*

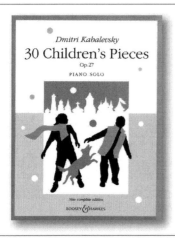

*Playing Ball (page 14) is taken from:*

**THIRTY CHILDREN'S PIECES, Op 27**
Dmitri Kabalevsky

ISMN 979-0-060-11230-0

Thirty imaginative pieces for developing young pianists to learn and enjoy.

*Dmitri Kabalevsky (1904–1987) was a prolific Russian composer whose work included four symphonies, five operas and eight concertos. He made a crucial impact on Soviet musical education and his songs and instrumental studies for children are now popular around the world.*

*Picnic Piece (page 22) is taken from:*

**MICROJAZZ COLLECTION 2**
Christopher Norton

ISMN 979-0-060-12251-4 (includes CD containing performance and backing tracks)

Christopher Norton's acclaimed **microjazz** series has won worldwide popularity with teachers and students alike for its stimulating blend of contemporary genres and classical values.

*Christopher Norton is an established composer, arranger, educationalist and producer, and has written stage musicals, ballet scores, popular songs and orchestral music as well as jingles and signature tunes for TV and radio.*